The little book of friendship

HAYDEN

Text and illustrations by Christine Coirault

for more books visit
www.frogillo.com/books

First published by Frogillo Books, 2008
Copyright Frogillo Books 2008

ISBN
0954854853
9780954854850

Hello!
Hayden
(your name here)
Pleased
to meet you!

You can never have too many friends!

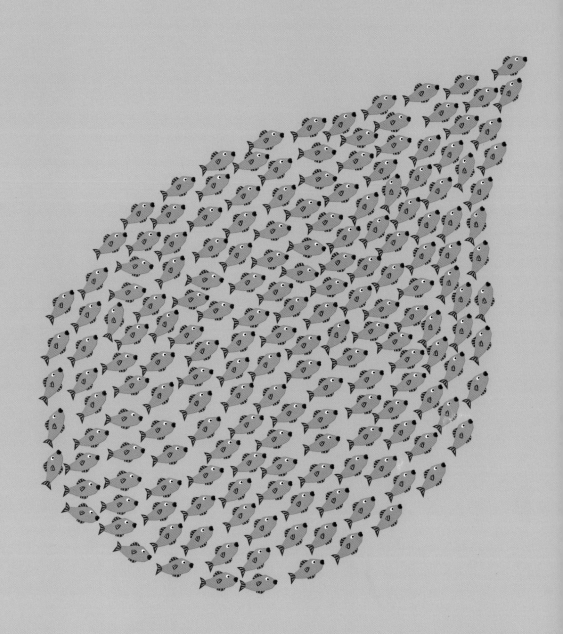

Friends do things together.

They play
together.

They look out

for each other.

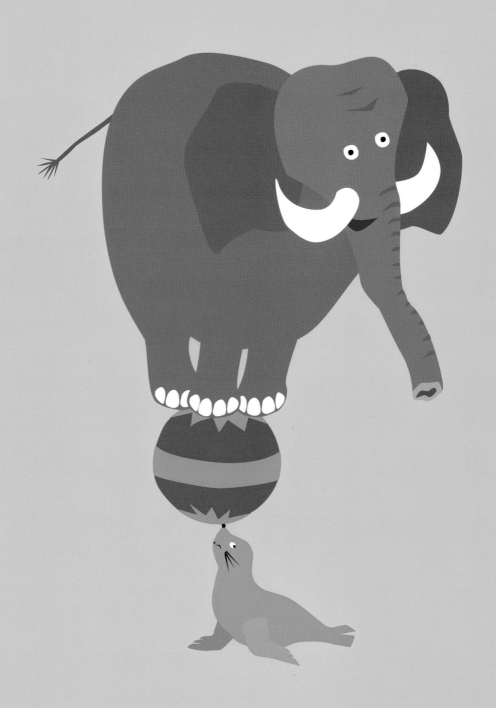

They
share their
favourite
things.

Friends
are
considerate
and
thoughtful.

They help
each other.

Friends are there

RTHDAY

for you... ....

...and you are

there for them!

Friends

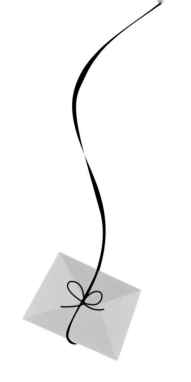

make an effort...

...to keep in touch.

Good friends...

...stick together...

...no matter what!

Goodbye for now!

The
little book
of
good manners

Christine Corault

9780954854805

The
little book
of
table manners

Christine Corault

9780954854829

The
little book
of
good
& behaviour

Christine Corault

9780954854812